Grade 4

The Syllabus of Examinations should be read for details of requirements, especially those for scales, aural tests and sight-reading. Attention should be paid to the Special Notices on the front inside cover, where warning is given of changes.

The syllabus is obtainable from music dealers or from The Associated Board of the Royal Schools of Music, 14 Bedford Square, London WC1B 3JG (please send stamped addressed envelope measuring about 9×6 ins.).

In overseas centres, information may be obtained from the Local Representative or Resident Secretary.

Requirements

SCALES, ARPEGGIOS AND BROKEN CHORDS
(from memory)

Scales
(i) in similar motion, hands together one octave apart, and each hand separately, in the following keys:
B, Bb, Eb, Ab, Db majors and C♯, G♯, C, F minors (melodic *or* harmonic minor at candidate's choice) (all two octaves)
(ii) in contrary motion, both hands beginning and ending on the key-note (unison), in the keys of F and Bb majors and D and G harmonic minors (two octaves)

Chromatic Scales
in similar motion, hands together one octave apart, and each hand separately, beginning on any black key named by the examiner (two octaves)

Arpeggios
(i) the common chords of E, B and F majors, in root position only, in similar motion, hands together one octave apart, and each hand separately (two octaves)
(ii) the common chords of Eb, Ab and Db majors, and C♯, G♯, C and F minors, in root position only, each hand separately (two octaves)

Broken Chords
formed from the chords of Bb major and G minor, each hand separately, according to both patterns shown in the syllabus

PLAYING BY SIGHT (see current syllabus)

AURAL TESTS (see current syllabus)

THREE PIECES

Candidates must prepare Nos.1 & 2 from the *same* list, A *or* B, but may choose No.3 from *either* list *or* one of the further alternatives listed below:

Skütte   Prelude in A minor, Op.51 No.1
Sartorio   Study in D minor, Op.1092 No.4
These are included in More Romantic Pieces for Piano, Book II, *published by the Associated Board*

Editor for the Associated Board: **Lionel Salter**

A:1
ALLEGRO in G

L. MOZART

This piece comes from a notebook that Leopold Mozart put together in 1759 for his 8-year-old daughter Nannerl. But, as the proud father recorded, her little brother learnt this Allegro (and nine other pieces) in his fourth year. All phrasing and dynamics here are editorial. The grace-notes should be played before the beat.   L.S.

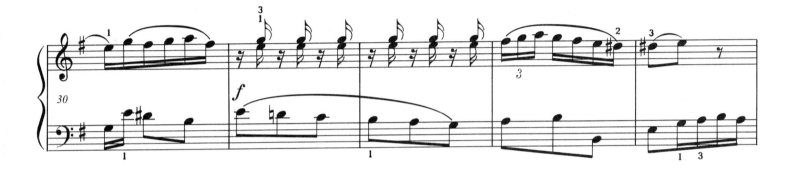

A:2
BAGATELLE in F

Edited by
Howard Ferguson

BEETHOVEN, Op.33 No.3

Source: [7] *Bagatelles* (Bureau d'Arts et d'Industrie, Vienna [1803]). Tovey wrote of these works that they are 'full of precisely the kind of wit and fancy that children can . . . enjoy, and that men of genius can retain throughout their lives'.

© 1981 by The Associated Board of the Royal Schools of Music
Reprinted from *A Keyboard Anthology*, 2nd Series, Book II, edited by Howard Ferguson (Associated Board)

AB 2352

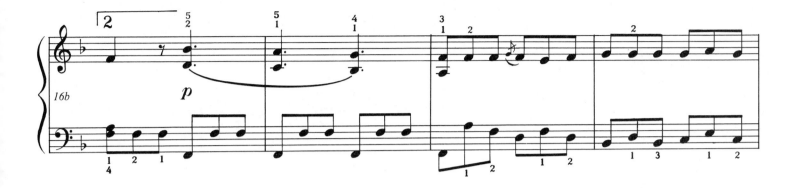

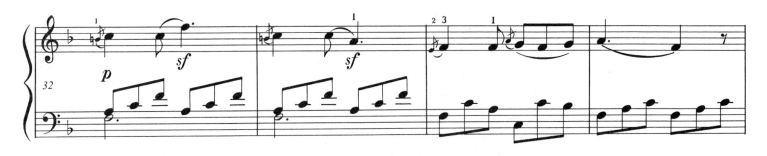

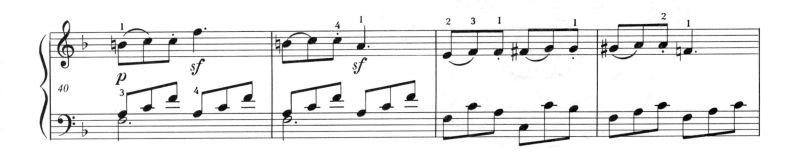

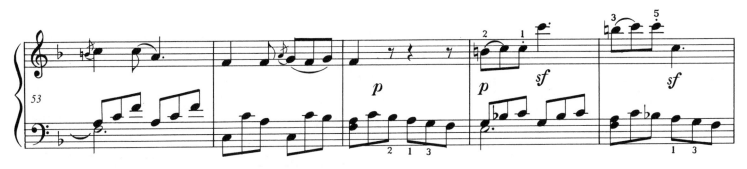

A:3
BALLABILE
(For Dancing)

HEINZ BENKER

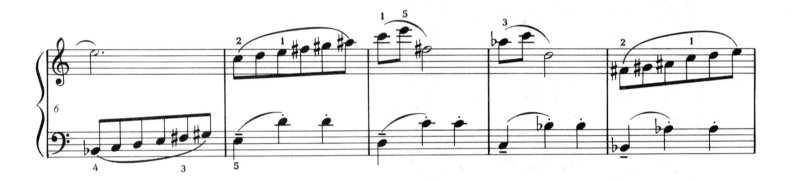

The composer suggests that dynamics should be left to the player's discretion.　L.S.

B:1
COURANTE in F

[**Allegro,** ♩ = 104]

HANDEL, HWV 488

The dynamics and phrasing (of which there is none in the original) are editorial. L.S.

B:2
BARCAROLLE

J.F.F. BURGMÜLLER, Op.100 No.22

Source: *25 Etudes faciles et progressives composées pour des petites mains*, Op.100 (London 1854). Though born in Germany, Burgmüller settled in Paris, where he wrote voluminously for the piano.   L.S.

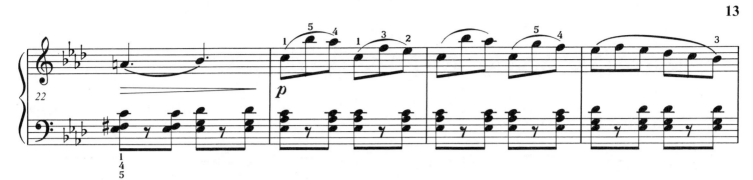

[1]caressingly [2]dying away

B:3
GRANDMAMA TELLS A GHOST STORY

KULLAK, Op.81 No.3

Theodor Kullak, one of a family of musicians, was a pupil of Czerny and became court pianist to the King of Prussia. He was a co-founder of a conservatory in Berlin in 1850, but, falling out with his partner, he set up a school of his own (also in Berlin) five years later.   L.S.

Reprinted from *Short Romantic Pieces for Piano*, Book II, edited by Lionel Salter (Associated Board)

AB 2352